Text: First Published in Great Britain in 2021

ISBN 978-1-8384970-0-2

Graphic design by Lanfranchi Graphic Design, UK, email lisalanfranchi@gmail.com

Printed and bound in Great Britain by
Sarsen Press, 22 Hyde Street, Winchester, Hampshire SO23 7DR

Buddy

and the English Lady

by Maggie Hampton

For Max, Charlotte, Joseph and Reuben.

Illustration by Allen Edwards

3

Just a word to say thank you

Thank you so much for purchasing this book. I am sure young family members (and not so young) will enjoy this wonderful story that transports its audience to rural Italy and the canine adventures with Buddy that await!

The author of this book, Maggie, is not only an excellent and creative writer, but also an exceptional member of our care team management at Rainbow Trust Children's Charity. The charity provides vital emotional and practical support to families with a seriously ill child, and we are incredibly grateful that Maggie has chosen to support us through the sale of her beautiful book.

Rainbow Trust supports almost 1,000 families across England and 97 families from our Essex Care Team where Maggie is based. Every book purchased will help us to continue providing support to families when their world has been turned upside down by a devastating diagnosis.

Please do spread the word about this book, buy it for friends and family, and know that every pound you kindly spend will help Rainbow Trust continue supporting families when they need it most.

I shall now "disappear" and let you enjoy the book!

Thank you,

Zillah Bingley

Chief Executive

Rainbow Trust Children's Charity

5

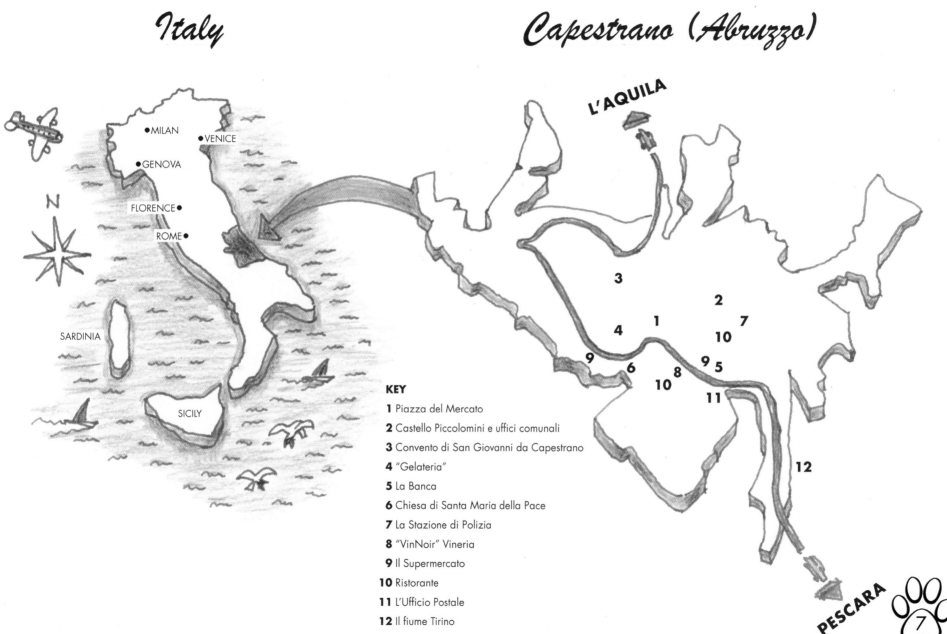

Italy

Capestrano (Abruzzo)

MILAN

VENICE

GENOVA

FLORENCE

ROME

SARDINIA

SICILY

N

L'AQUILA

PESCARA

KEY

1 Piazza del Mercato

2 Castello Piccolomini e uffici comunali

3 Convento di San Giovanni da Capestrano

4 "Gelateria"

5 La Banca

6 Chiesa di Santa Maria della Pace

7 La Stazione di Polizia

8 "VinNoir" Vineria

9 Il Supermercato

10 Ristorante

11 L'Ufficio Postale

12 Il fiume Tirino

It was a hot, sunny day in September when the English lady first noticed a strange dog outside her gate.

She was living alone, renovating a house, on the edge of a medieval village in Italy.

This bedraggled, very sad looking animal seemed friendly enough but in a timid kind of way.

He had a long, black coat and tan eyebrows which gave him a permanent, quizzical expression.

Permesso?

The lady opened the gate and they walked up to the house together. The dog just sat there, waiting patiently.

Feeling sorry for him, she immediately wanted to help. He was very thin so she thought he might be hungry.

10

The lady found some leftover cornflakes and milk which were soon demolished,
rapidly but politely, until the dish was licked clean.

Then the dog just turned around… **and disappeared!**

The very next day, he was back, waiting expectantly at the gate. This went on for the next few days.

He would turn up for his breakfast...
and then disappear!

The lady found out he was a stray hunting dog who was being fed by some kind people in the village.

However, no-one actually owned him so she knew he needed a good home.

Pleased to have a new friend, the lady called him *Buddy*.

É molto bello qui!

First things first, if *Buddy* wanted to come in the house, he desperately needed a bath.

Filling the tub with warm water, the lady gingerly lifted him in.

She expected him to fly straight out again, but, surprisingly, he seemed to enjoy it.

A whole bottle of doggie shampoo later and he was finally clean.

Of course, he shook himself all over the bathroom.

Then he ran outside, round and round the patio, trying to get himself dry but before she could catch him...

... he disappeared!

Another day passed and *Buddy* was back.

The next hurdle was to get rid of all the knots in his fur; the long hair on his ears was tangled into solid clumps.

So, after some help from a friend with some sharp scissors, *Buddy* had a drastic but necessary haircut.

All the matted hair had to be cut off and eventually...

... he stood there patiently, enjoying the attention. Afterwards, he looked like a brand new dog and much more comfortable without the bits of brambles and who knows what stuck in his hair.

To celebrate... **he disappeared!**

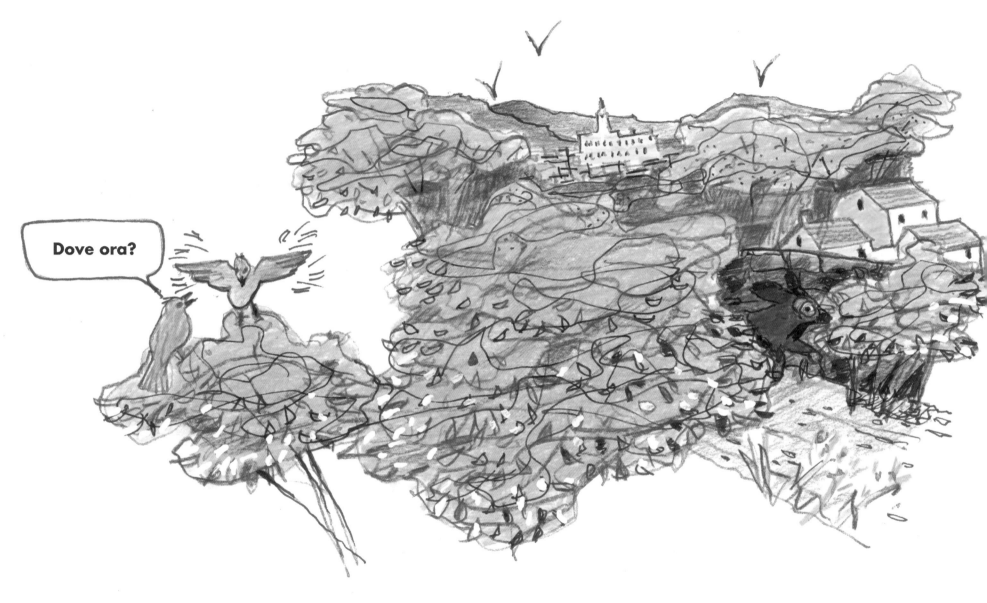

Buddy is sneaking out **AGAIN!**

Can you see him?

The lady's Italian neighbour said that if she planned on keeping him, he should be checked over by a vet... vaccinated, wormed and microchipped.

Il veterinario sta arrivando

The vet turned up that very day.

At first, *Buddy* was nervous and hid under the table.

22

A bit of coaxing and one hundred and twenty euros later, the vet said that *Buddy* was ready to go.

Buddy was listening as, no sooner had the vet left…

Guardami adesso. Bravo eh?

Perfetto amico mio

23

... **he disappeared** to find a
sunny spot for a nap. The day had
just been too exhausting!

Buddy's vanishing act became a routine.

As soon as the lady let him out of the house
in the morning, he would disappear, sometimes
for several hours, but always he came back,
happy to lie in the sun for the rest of the day.

Finding out that farmers were known to shoot trespassing, stray dogs, the lady felt *Buddy* needed to stay home with her full time.

So, she started to secure his outside space, but each time she thought she had finished, he found another way out... and **disappeared!**

25

Finally, with all escape routes blocked, *Buddy*'s adventures were limited to long walks with the English lady, roaming the vineyards that surrounded the village.

With very few cars on the road, *Buddy* was able to run free, although it proved rather tricky getting him back on a lead as we all now know... he liked to **disappear!**

Often, the pair went down to the river so *Buddy* could have a swim and cool off. He loved fetching sticks and would stay there all day if the lady let him.

They became good pals as they settled into their new way of life together, but every now and again, *Buddy* managed **to escape**…

... and ... DISAPPEARED !

Christmas was approaching and the lady's family arrived for a visit.

Suddenly, the house was filled with joy and laughter. This was great for the English lady but she was not sure about *Buddy*.

His favourite place on the sofa was taken and he was relegated to the floor. He ate far too much and was becoming fed up with the guests.

The family actually grew fond of *Buddy* and named him "Elvis" as his lip used to curl against his teeth "**Uh-huh**".

Buddy took exception to being laughed at and after that he spent quite a lot of time outside!

The lady thought he was pleased when the family went skiing and left him in peace.

All too soon it was just him and her again.

Cold weather was forecast for the New Year. *Buddy* and the lady woke up to find a metre of snow outside the front door.

Thinking *Buddy* would like to get outside, she dug a path as far as the driveway, but unusually, for once, her friend didn't bolt out the door to play...

... but turned and retreated to his favourite spot on the sofa.
They were stuck indoors for uno... due... tre... long...
long... weeks!

33

Eventually, there was a slight thaw so *Buddy* and the lady went outside to help their neighbours dig away the snow.

Buddy sniffed the cold air, wondering what to do...?

The English lady's time in Italy was coming to an end and she needed to return to England.

Sadly, she knew that *Buddy*, her free spirit, would not be happy living in a rainy, busy, noisy city like London.

What a dilemma!

Desperate to find her furry friend a good home, she put a picture and description of *Buddy* on a website which re-homes dogs in Italy.

Fortunately, a couple said they would like to have him.

Buddy would be happy there as they had a huge garden, no children and they absolutely adored dogs.

Packing up *Buddy* and all his belongings, the English lady and her pal set off in the car for the 200 kilometre trip to his new home.

On arrival, *Buddy* eagerly jumped out the car and was introduced to his new owners. The couple were so excited to see him, they couldn't wait to show him around.

Sadly, the lady didn't get to say goodbye to *Buddy* as he was busy with his new best friends, so she took her chance and...

...she disappeared!

Buddy and the English Lady is a true story: In the summer of 2011, I took a year off work to renovate an old farmhouse in the beautiful countryside of Abruzzo.

My "guardian angel" appeared at my gate when he was most needed.
The rest of the story you already know... *Buddy* settled very happily into his new home in Le Marche and, true to character, is moving into old age **very** disgracefully.

If you enjoyed reading this....and learning some Italian, then look out for *Buddy*'s next adventures in my new book... COMING SOON.

My grateful thanks to all those who contributed their time, patience and expertise to the production of this book. I would also like to thank SS&C Charity Committee for their generous sponsorship which has enabled publication.

Best wishes

All profits from this book will be donated to
Rainbow Trust Children's Charity, Registered Charity No 1070532
Further information on the valuable support Rainbow Trust gives to families with seriously ill children can be found at www.rainbowtrust.org.uk.

THE END

BUDDY'S ITALIAN-ENGLISH PHRASEBOOK